THE
BLACK-EYED
GIRL

Titles in Dark Reads:

Badger Publishing Limited, Oldmedow Road, Hardwick Industrial Estate, King's Lynn PE30 4JJ
Telephone: 01438 791037

www.badgerlearning.co.uk

THE BLACK-EYED GIRL

TIM COLLINS

The Black-Eyed Girl ISBN 978-1-78464-091-0

Publisher: Susan Ross
Senior Editor: Danny Pearson
Publishing Assistant: Claire Morgan
Copyeditor: Cheryl Lanyon
Designer: Bigtop Design Ltd
Illustrator: Mark Penman

2 4 6 8 10 9 7 5 3 1

Printed by Bell and Bain Ltd, Glasgow

CHAPTER 1
THE BASEMENT

No one ever uses the toilets in
the basement.

They are meant to be haunted
by a girl with black eyes.

She appears if you look in the mirror
and blink three times.

I did not believe it. Until I tried it.

I went down one night with my friends
Megan and Lauren.

The floor was slippery and there was
a damp, stale smell.

I wondered if one of the toilets
was leaking.

Megan pointed to the dusty mirror.

"That's where the ghost lives," she said.
"She died falling down the stairs. They say
she appears all white except for her piercing
black eyes."

Lauren walked up to the mirror and wiped
it with her sleeve.

I stepped up to the mirror and felt my heart racing.

"After three," said Megan. "1… 2… 3…"

I closed and opened my eyes three times and stared deep into the reflection.

I could see something behind us. It was a small, white shape… and two burning black eyes.

It lunged forwards and I glimpsed a tiny, white hand.

CHAPTER 2
BLACK TEARS

When I turned around there was no one there. But I could still see that ghostly hand in my mind.

Lauren didn't see anything. Megan didn't see anything. But I know I did.

I vowed never to return to the basement.

But my problems did not stop there.

I spotted something in the mirror while I was brushing my teeth that night.

A girl in a filthy white dress was cowering in the corner of the bathroom.

She looked up.

Her eyes were pitch black, with no whites and no irises.

She made a grab for me.

I turned around and she was gone.

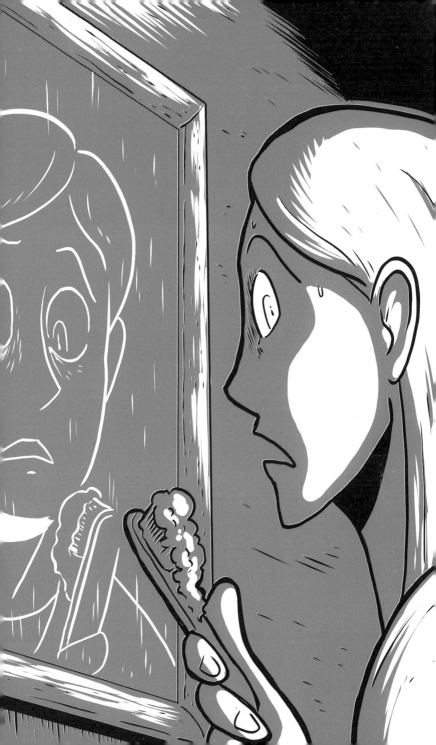

I saw her in my bedroom mirror the next morning.

She was crawling over the bed with her arm stretched out.

Black tears were leaking down her cheeks and her lips were moving silently.

I saw the ghost everywhere on my way to school.

I glimpsed her pale hand in a car's side mirror.

I saw her white face floating behind me in the glass of my phone.

I even spotted her dark, bleeding eyes looking over my shoulder as I stared out the bus window.

I got off at the next stop and ran the rest of the way.

CHAPTER 3
REACHING OUT

I told Lauren and Megan about it in our PE lesson.

"The ghost wants you to do something," said Megan. "You need to talk to her."

"Ghosts have unfinished business," said Lauren. "If you help them they leave you in peace."

I thought about it. Every time I'd seen the girl she'd been reaching out.

But I'd always turned around before she could get to me.

If I waited for her to touch me, she might still be there when I turned. Then I could find out what she wanted.

I went back down to the basement toilets.

I blinked three times.

The girl appeared in the mirror, scuttling behind me.

I really wanted to turn round, but I forced myself to keep looking at her.

The girl smiled as she got closer and closer.

I felt the tips of her fingers on my neck.

CHAPTER 4
STUCK

I looked around. The girl was gone.

After all I'd put myself through, I still couldn't find out what she wanted.

Then I turned back to the mirror and screamed.

My eyes had been replaced by patches of black.

I looked down at my feet. They were floating off the floor.

I tried to open the door, but my hand went through the handle.

I began to cry, and black tears rolled down my cheeks.

Now I'm stuck here in the basement toilets, waiting for someone to come in and blink three times.

GHOSTS

In 2014, several people claimed to have seen a black-eyed ghost girl in Cannock Chase, Staffordshire. A similar figure had been spotted 30 years earlier.

Several ghosts are linked with mirrors. A popular myth tells of a ghost named Bloody Mary. She will appear if you look in a mirror and say her name three times.

In Japanese legend, a spirit named 'Hanako-San' haunts school toilets. You can call her by going to the third stall along in the third floor toilet and knocking three times.

In 2013 a painter tried to sell a haunted mirror on eBay. He claimed it had given him nightmares and stabbing pains.

QUESTIONS

How many times do you need to
blink in order for the girl to appear?
(page 5)

How did the girl in the mirror die?
(page 8)

What was the girl in the mirror wearing?
(page 14)

What lesson did the girls meet up in?
(page 20)

How many times do you need to say
Bloody Mary for her to appear?
(page 30)

In what year did someone try to sell
a haunted mirror on eBay?
(page 30)

Tim Collins has written over 40 books for children and adults, including *Wimpy Vampire*, *Cosmic Colin* and *Dorkius Maximus*. His other titles for Badger Learning include *Dawn of the Daves*, *Troll*, *The Locals* and *Joke Shop*.

Mark Penman thinks he maybe played one too many fantasy games (on his computer). Now it seems he can only silence the terrifying voices in his head by drawing scary stories starring terrified teens.